EGMONT

We bring stories to life

First published in Great Britain 1997 by Egmont UK Limited
This edition published 2018 by Dean,
an imprint of Egmont UK Limited,
The Yellow Building, 1 Nicholas Road, London, W11 4AN
www.egmont.co.uk

ISBN 978 0 6035 7572 3

70172/001

Printed in Malaysia

A CIP catalogue record for this title is available from the British Library.

Stay safe online. Egmont is not responsible for content hosted by third parties.

Egmont takes its responsibility to the planet and its inhabitants very seriously.
All the papers we use are from well-managed forests run by responsible suppliers.

What's my favourite colour?

Is it Green?

Green is the grass

where I like to walk.

Is it
Pink?

Pink are the petals
of my favourite
flowers.

Is it *Black*?
Black is the night
when bats swoop
and soar.

Is it Red?
Red is the rug
where I snooze
by the fire.

Is it **Yellow?**

Yellow is the sand on the sunny beach.

Is it Blue?
Blue is the sky where
I chase the birds.

Is it White?

White are the clouds floating in the sky.

Is it Orange?

Yes! Because...

Orange is the colour of Mummy.

What colour is your favourite?

Green?

Pink?

Black?

Red?

Look at Cat's different colours!

Green

Pink

Black

Red

Purple

Gellow

White

Blue

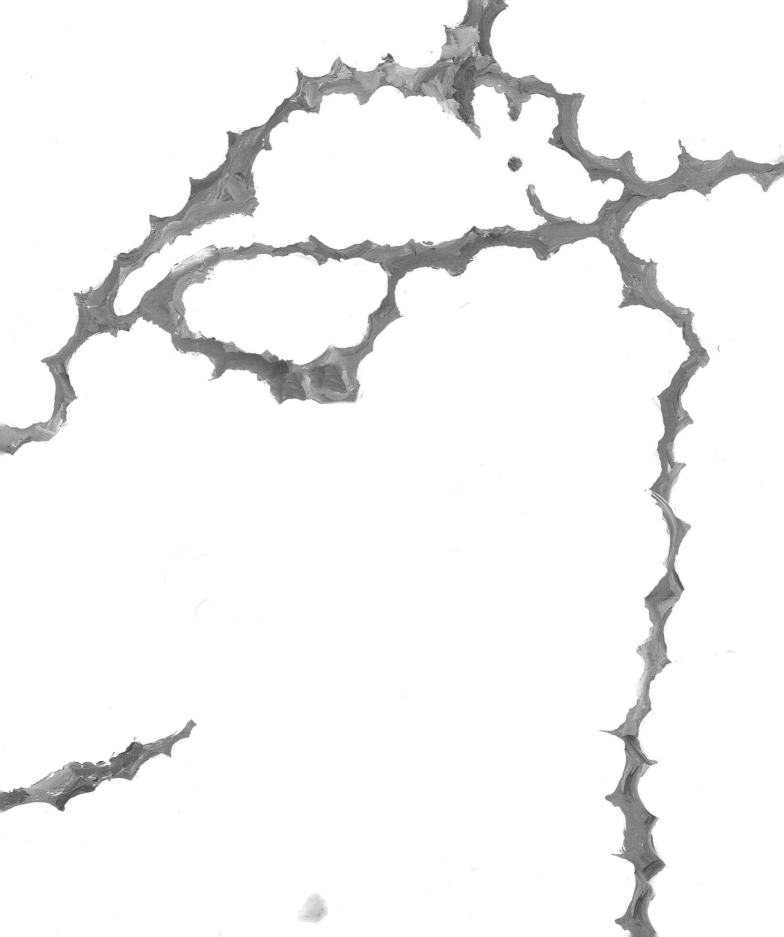